The House of the Seven Gables

Nathaniel Hawthorne

Academic Industries, Inc.
West Haven, Connecticut 06516

ISBN 0-88301-728-8

Published by
Academic Industries, Inc.
The Academic Building
Saw Mill Road
West Haven, Connecticut 06516

Printed in the United States of America

about the author

Nathaniel Hawthorne, an American romance writer, was born in Salem, Massachusetts in 1804. He was educated at Bowdoin College in Maine and was the most distinguished craftsman of the New England school of letters. He led a quiet life, removed from the activities of his times, in a restless solitude. Because of his passionless upbringing, he had a strong pride and sense of alienation from the world in which he lived.

At age forty-five he wrote a story which had long been stored in his mind—*The Scarlet Letter*. Written with intense gloom and great indifference, Hawthorne's restlessness can easily be felt throughout the novel. *The House of the Seven Gables,* his second work, reveals a variety of moods and thus is perhaps more characteristic of Hawthorne. In this novel he shows how the secrets of an old and mysterious house can control the people who live there.

Even though Hawthorne's concern is always with what is ethical, only rarely does his imagination join with creative passion. More frequently you will find just a hint of emotion.

Nathaniel Hawthorne

THE HOUSE
OF THE
SEVEN GABLES

Phoebe
Pyncheon

Mr. Holgrave

Hepzibah
Pyncheon

Colonel Pyncheon

Judge
Jaffrey
Pyncheon

Clifford
Pyncheon

Uncle
Venner

For nearly two hundred years, the Pyncheon family had owned and lived in the House of the Seven Gables . . .

The family was under a curse put upon them by old Matthew Maule. As he stood ready to be hanged for witchcraft, Maule cried out to Colonel Pyncheon, "God will give you blood to drink!"

In forty years, with the growth of the town, Maule's land had become a valuable piece of property.

A good spot for the family house I plan to build!

Will Maule sell it to you?

I believe my family has a claim to that land! Of course I will pay Maule something for his work.

Old Maule is stubborn! You'll have a fight on your hands.

We'll see what the courts have to say about that!

But Colonel Pyncheon was not able to prove his claim. Then came the day that Matthew Maule was tried for witchcraft.

Matthew Maule, you will be taken to Gallows Hill and hanged!

Pyncheon wants Maule's land—and he spoke out most strongly against him!

Shhh! It's not safe to say such things!

It was Colonel Pyncheon to whom Maule spoke just before he was hanged.

God will give you blood to drink!

Then the land passed to Colonel Pyncheon. The people of the village talked about his plans.

The colonel's got nerve, all right—building his family home right on top of old Maule's little house.

Almost like building on a grave!

Why, it's like inviting Maule's ghost right in!

Oh, no! The colonel's too smart to worry about ghosts!

It was a strange fact that the spring water, sweet for so many years, became hard and bitter.

What's happened to Maule's spring?

Digging the deeper cellar must have spoiled the water!

Maybe that . . . maybe something worse! But I know it will make you sick if you drink it!

And another fact made people talk.

There he is—Thomas Maule! Pyncheon hired old Matthew's son to build his house!

Makes sense! Thomas Maule is the best workman around here!

And why shouldn't the Maules make some money out of it?

As builder of the House of the Seven Gables, Thomas Maule did a fine job. When it was finished, Colonel Pyncheon invited the whole town to be his guests. There was to be a service first, and then a great meal.

The Reverend Mr. Higginson is to give a talk.

Ale, cider, wine, and brandy for all! That's what I like!

And a roasted ox—and a deer—and codfish chowder! I smell 'em cooking!

Inside the great front doors, servants showed some people toward the kitchen. Others were led into the grander rooms.

Through here, sir.

This way, my man.

But something was wrong. The high-sheriff of the county spoke to one of the servants.

Where is Colonel Pyncheon? The most important people are arriving!

Here is the Lieutenant-governor! Call Colonel Pyncheon at once!

I know he wanted time to be alone. But he will not be pleased if you allow him to miss one of our chief rulers! Call him right away!

I cannot do that. My master demands that I obey him. You open that door yourself.

Never mind, Master High-sheriff! It is indeed time the colonel came forth to greet his friends. I will call him.

That should do it!

The Lieutenant-governor knocked hard on the door.

There was no answer. He knocked again.

Perhaps he has taken a sip too much of his wine in honor of the day!

Angry now, the Lieutenant-governor banged on the door with the heavy side of his sword.

That noise is enough to wake the dead!

But still no answer. He tried the door. It was flung wide by a gust of wind that rushed through the room, blowing the ladies' skirts and the curls of the gentlemen's wigs.

Strange . . . very strange!

Then people pressed forward. At first everything looked normal.

He looks angry!

The colonel's little grandson ran toward the seated figure.

Grandpa! Grandpa!

Halfway he stopped, afraid.

Then, crying, he ran away.

Mama! Mama!

The guests moved closer and all became clear.

Dead! Colonel Pyncheon's dead!

Dead, in his new home!

There was blood on his collar and his beard was soaked with it.

Old Maule's curse came true! God has given him blood to drink!

Many reasons were given for his death.

They say there were finger marks on his throat!

And a bloody handprint on his collar! That's what I heard!

A window near him was open . . . and someone saw a man climbing over the garden wall and running away.

But the important doctors who talked over the case were sure of what they said.

No question, gentlemen. It is a clear case of apoplexy!

Agreed, sir!

And no one could argue with the statement of the coroner's jury.

You have decided already?

Yes, sir . . . sudden death from natural causes!

Colonel Pyncheon left a great deal of property. His lawyer called on his son to discuss it.

Now, your father claimed a large piece of land in Maine. It has not been proven that he owned it.

It is a very large piece of land, with silver and who knows what else. All we Pyncheons have heard of it!

I know. He bought it from an Indian. The court said it would be legal as long as he had a paper to prove the sale.

But no signed paper had ever been found, and the Pyncheons had only the map on the wall to remind them of it.

The years passed. Many Pyncheons were born and died, until only five remained. The House of the Seven Gables grew old. Old Miss Hepzibah Pyncheon now lived there almost alone.

One day at sunrise she arose, dressed, and knelt at her prayers.

With your help, Lord, I will be able to do it!

Finishing, she took from a drawer a picture of a very handsome young man.

I *must* do it — for your sake, Clifford!

Replacing the picture, she moved to a looking glass to wipe away a few tears.

She made her way downstairs through shadowy hallways into a dark room.

A shop! Whatever would Colonel Pyncheon say if he were alive!

Nearly a century before, one of the Pyncheons had opened a shop on the first floor of the house. Since his death, it had gathered dust until only a few days ago. But then Hepzibah had cleaned it and stocked it with food and other goods. Now she went there.

The window! I must put some gingerbread cookies in the shop window!

Miss Hepzibah jumped back in fright as the bell over the shop door jingled.

My dear Miss Pyncheon, you are carrying out your idea! I look in to offer my good wishes!

Mr. Holgrave, I can't go through with it! Never, never, never!

I wish I were dead and in the family tomb! The world is too hard—and I am too old, too hopeless!

Believe me, these feelings will not trouble you once you are really into your work!

This is a lucky day! Your blood has been chilling in your veins too long! Now you join the world in a healthy effort!

But you are a man, Mr. Holgrave! I was born a lady . . .

No lady of your family has done a braver thing since the house was built!

These are new ideas! I don't understand them!

Now I must be your first customer! Half-a-dozen of those rolls . . .

Let me be a lady a moment longer! I must not receive money from my only friend.

When Holgrave left, Miss Pyncheon felt a little more cheerful. Then she heard talking at the shop door.

What a sight! In the old Pyncheon house, under the Pyncheon elm, old maid Pyncheon setting up a shop!

Will she do well, do you think? There's another shop just around the corner.

Never! Her frown is enough to frighten away all the customers!

My wife kept a shop for three months and lost $5.00!

Oh! What am I to do? How can I hope to succeed!

Again she was startled by the shop bell over her head.

Ting-a-ling!

Heaven help me!

Looking over the counter, she saw her first customer.

Well, child . . .

What do you want?

That gingerbread man in the window!

Miss Pyncheon took the gingerbread man from the window, and the boy held out his penny.

You are welcome to the gingerbread. Keep your penny!

Moving to shut the door after him, Miss Pyncheon saw the small boy outside eating the gingerbread man.

Small boys! Never shut a door . . . always hungry . . .

Hardly had she put another gingerbread man in the window when the bell rang again.

Well, what now?

I want that other gingerbread man.

Here it is for you. Where is your penny?

I have it.

The boy left. Miss Hepzibah dropped her first money into the cash drawer.

It is done! I am no longer a Pyncheon lady. I am an old maid shopkeeper!

24

More customers came. Some were happy, others not.

No ginger beer? No root beer? No tobacco? What kind of shop do you keep?

A shop without yeast? You might as well close at once!

Well, perhaps I should.

Around noon, a gentleman stopped across the street to look at the shop.

Catching sight of Hepzibah's face in the shop window, his frown changed to a smile and he bowed.

H'm . . .

Hello, Cousin Jaffrey! You have seen my little shop window!

This was Judge Jaffrey Pyncheon, a rich member of the family.

Moving to the back parlor, Hepzibah stopped to study the old picture.

Let Jaffrey smile as he will. He looks like old Colonel Pyncheon!

Take it as you like! What have you to say about it? Pyncheon House is mine while I am alive!

He has proved himself the very man to build a new house! Perhaps, too, the man to draw down a new curse!

Called back to the shop again by the bell, Hepzibah found there a very old man known as Uncle Venner.

So, you have really opened your shop! Well, I'm glad to see it. Young folks should never be idle . . .

Nor old ones, either, for that matter. But if I should get sick I'll go to a farm and retire!

It seems to me I have just begun work when I should be giving it up! Perhaps I'll retire with you to the old folks' home!

Did I say farm? The old folks' home is more like it!

Just then, with much feeling in his old face, Venner whispered to Hepzibah.

When do you expect him home?

Oh! Whom do you mean?

You don't want to talk of it! We'll say no more . . . though the word's all over town. I remember him before he could run alone . . . and you, too, Hepzibah!

27

Hepzibah went through the rest of the day in a daze, making mistakes with all her customers. But at last she could muffle the bell and put up the bar across the door. As she did so, she saw a coach stop under the elm tree.

Is it he? Am I to meet him now?

But it was a slender young girl who was helped from the coach. Her luggage was brought to the front door.

There, miss— that will bring someone!

Thank you!

Can it be Cousin Phoebe? Well, I suppose she must stay here overnight!

But it must be only to-night! If Clifford were to find her here, it might disturb him!

Early next morning, Hepzibah called Phoebe into her room.

Phoebe, this is a sad house for a young person. It lets in the wind and rain and snow, but never the sun! And I am a bad-tempered old woman!

I think we may suit one another better than you suppose.

So it was that Phoebe, one of the last Pyncheons, arrived at the House of the Seven Gables. The recent remarriage of her mother had sent Phoebe in search of a new home. It was natural to come to a near relative for a week's visit. And she could always stay longer if both of them were happy.

I cannot make your life happy. I can't so much as give you bread to eat!

You will find me a cheerful little person. And I mean to earn my bread!

But after all, child, it is not for me to say who shall live in the old Pyncheon house. Its master is coming.

Do you mean Judge Pyncheon?

29

Judge Pyncheon! He will hardly come here while I live if I can help it!

Then who . . .

Rushing away, Hepzibah brought back the picture she loved.

Here it is—the face of the one I mean!

Very handsome!

Do you like the face?

It is as good a face as a man's can be . . . with something of a child about it. One feels so very kindly toward him!

He ought never to suffer. One would do much to spare him. Who is it, Cousin Hepzibah?

Did you ever hear of Clifford Pyncheon?

Never! And yet . . . I seem to have heard the name from my father. Is he not a long time dead?

Well, child, perhaps he is. But in old houses like this, dead people are likely to come back again. We shall see!

And since you are not afraid after all I've said, we will not part so soon.

You are welcome to such a home as I can offer you!

Thank you, Cousin Hepzibah!

Downstairs as they sat at breakfast, the shop bell rang.

The shop! I must go . . .

Do not trouble yourself. I am shopkeeper today!

You, child? What can you know of such matters?

I have done all the shopping for the family. You'll see that I am a good little saleswoman!

Indeed, during the day she took care of all the customers. Later she had suggestions to make.

I can make yeast, and I brew root beer. I can also make spice cakes which will sell . . .

We need more gingerbread figures, and toys . . . and candy . . .

People want cheap raisins . . . and we must have a peck of apples!

Uncle Venner, who had been in and out during the day, now returned.

Look! A regular mountain of pennies!

Well done! Here's a girl who will never end her days at my farm!

Yes, Phoebe is a good girl!

Later Hepzibah led Phoebe from room to room, telling her the family stories.

Here are the dents made by the Lieutenant-governor's sword when Colonel Pyncheon sat dead on the other side of the door!

She had Phoebe stand on a chair to look at the map of the Pyncheon land in Maine.

Upstairs she pointed out an old harpsichord.

Not only is the land valuable, but there is a silver mine! We'll be rich when the government agrees on the Pyncheon claim!

It belonged to Alice Pyncheon, who lived and died a hundred years ago.

But is it never opened and played upon?

Oh, no, my dear! Alice was beautiful and talented. But she died while she was still very young. Some people say she lives here yet!

Moving on, Hepzibah pointed out a locked door leading into a separate part of the house.

Through there are the rooms of Mr. Holgrave, the daguerreotypist.

Is he a nice young man?

He seems quiet and well-meaning. But he has the strangest friends—men with long beards. They know no law and eat strange foods . . .

But, dear cousin, why do you let him stay?

Why, without exactly liking him, I would be sorry to see him go somewhere else to live.

A country girl, Phoebe loved the out-of-doors. In the early evening she walked in the garden.

I wonder who cares for the garden. Surely not Cousin Hepzibah!

In a corner, she saw a chicken coop.

What funny chickens! I am ashamed to think it, but the hens look a lot like Cousin Hepzibah!

A chick slipped between the bars and fluttered up to perch on Phoebe's shoulder.

What an odd chick you are! Here are some crumbs for you.

Suddenly, to Phoebe's surprise, a young man appeared behind her. He came from a door in one of the gables.

These birds are a special breed handed down in the Pyncheon family.

He treats you like an old friend. He must know you are a Pyncheon.

I am Phoebe Pyncheon. Do you take care of Cousin Hepzibah's garden?

Yes, I dig and hoe for fun. Otherwise, I make pictures. But I would be glad to turn over the flowers and these chickens to your care.

I will bring to Miss Hepzibah's table some good, honest kitchen vegetables. We will work together in this garden.

To her surprise, as night came on, Phoebe found herself weeding a flower bed. And she felt quite friendly with the young man.

Good night. Miss Phoebe Pyncheon! Any bright day, if you will put a rosebud in your hair, I will make a picture of the flower and its wearer!

Phoebe went into the dark house and said goodnight to Hepzibah.

My dear little girl, go to bed. I must sit awhile and think.

Good night, cousin. If you begin to love me, I am glad!

Sometime during the night Phoebe woke to hear footsteps on the stairs, and voices.

It's Hepzibah . . . but someone else too . . . or am I dreaming?

And Phoebe went back to sleep.

The next morning when she came down, the breakfast table was set with china and silver—for three people!

Bear with me, dear child! My heart is full to the brim!

My dearest cousin, what has happened?

Hush! He is coming! Let him see you first. He always liked bright faces! Poor Clifford!

There were footsteps on the stairs like those Phoebe had heard during the night. They came near and stopped. The knob turned. At last, unable to stand it any longer, Hepzibah rushed forward, flung open the door, and let into the room a stranger.

Dear Clifford, this is Phoebe, Arthur's only child. She has come to stay with us a while.

Phoebe? Arthur's child? Ah, I forget . . . but no matter! She is very welcome!

Hepzibah led Clifford to his place.

Come, dear Clifford. Take this chair and let us begin breakfast.

Clifford stared around the room as if he did not know where he was.

Phoebe studied his face. She knew she had seen it before.

The face in Hepzibah's picture! That's who it is!

But how old and worn he looks!

Coffee, my dear.

Is that you, Hepzibah? Are you angry with me? Why do you frown?

Angry with you, Clifford! There is nothing but love here! You are home!

How nice this is! The sunshine through the window . . . the young girl's face . . . it must be a dream!

Then Clifford saw the picture of old Colonel Pyncheon.

Hepzibah, that picture! It is the evil spirit of the house. Take it down!

I can't do that!

Then cover it with a curtain! It must not stare me in the face!

Yes, dear Clifford. It shall be covered. Phoebe and I will do it this very day!

Suddenly the sound of the shop bell was heard.

Good heavens. Hepzibah! What noises have we in the house?

That noise is nothing but our shop bell.

I will run to answer it!

Dear Clifford, we are very poor. I have opened a little shop in the front gable. Are you ashamed of me?

Shame? What shame can happen to me now?

Finally, his chair being deep and soft, Clifford fell asleep.

I will pull down the curtain and let him sleep.

In the shop, Phoebe found a well-dressed gentlemen with a gold-headed cane. He looked surprised at not seeing Hepzibah.

Ah! You are Miss Pyncheon's helper?

I am . . . and also her cousin. I am here on a visit.

Then I too am related to you! Surely you have heard of Judge Pyncheon?

I shall step in and see if Hepzibah and Clifford are in the parlor.

Phoebe moved toward the door to keep him from entering. But Judge Pyncheon, with a black frown, pushed her aside.

Perhaps, sir, I should call my cousin . . .

No, no! Stay where you are!

Woman, take care! Clifford is on the brink of ruin!

But why do I talk with you? Make way—I must see Clifford!

As the Judge moved forward to force his way, Clifford's weak, frightened voice came from inside.

Hepzibah, go down on your knees! Beg him not to come in! Keep him away!

With poor Clifford so unhappy, I must not see him now. But I shall watch him.

With a bow to Hepzibah and a nod for Phoebe, the judge went smiling down the street. Hepzibah, turning white, walked over to Phoebe and placed her head on Phoebe's shoulder.

That man has been the nightmare of my life. Shall I never have the courage to tell him what he is?

Is he so very evil?

Surely his offers were kind?

Don't speak of them! He has a heart of iron! Go, dear child, to Clifford. I am too upset.

Shall I read to you?

Yes, dear Phoebe. Your voice calms me!

Phoebe soon grew important to the happiness of her two cousins. Her kindness was just what Clifford needed to bring him back into the world. In the afternoons, while Hepzibah kept the shop, Phoebe took him into the garden.

Once a scissors-grinder set his wheel going. Children came running with the family scissors or knives to be sharpened.

An Italian boy came with his barrel-organ and monkey.

One morning Clifford sat in the window blowing soap bubbles into the street below.

He loved to do that when we were children.

The only young face Phoebe saw was the young daguerreotypist's. They held long talks together and became friends. One moonlight night they met in the garden.

Miss Hepzibah tells me that you go back to the country in a few days.

Yes, but only for a short visit. I look on this as my home now.

Good! I have a feeling the two-hundred-year-old drama played in this house is drawing to a close.

What do you mean? Do you know of some trouble for my cousins?

If so, tell me and I will stay!

I know nothing. It is only a feeling. And I promise to help them any way I can!

Two days later Phoebe left for the railroad station.

We shall miss you. Come back soon!

Very soon, Uncle Venner.

A storm brought days of wind and rain.

It seems as if the very house shakes in the wind.

On the fifth day, Clifford refused to leave his bed.

Very well, my dear . . . you're better off there!

The bell brought Hepzibah into her shop.

Cousin Jaffrey!

How are you, cousin? I've come to see Clifford!

49

You can't see him. He is in bed.

What? Then I *must* see him! Is he ill?

What if he should die?

He is in no danger—unless you bother him now. You nearly caused his death those many years ago.

Woman, it is I who had Clifford set free! And if he does not now tell me his secret, I will have him sent to an insane asylum for the rest of his life!

It is you, cousin, who are insane! Clifford knows no secret!

Thirty years ago when our uncle Jaffrey died, much of his money was missing! Clifford boasted to me that he knew where to find it! He must tell me the secret!

Sadly, Hepzibah went to call Clifford. The judge went into the parlor to wait, and sat down in Colonel Pyncheon's great chair.

Tell Clifford to come quickly! I have important things to do later today.

Hepzibah knocked at Clifford's door.

Clifford—dear brother? May I enter?

Rap-rap!

Clifford! He is gone!

She searched the house, looked into the garden. There was no sign of him!

He is gone! What will happen to him? Jaffrey must help me search!

She threw open the door into the dark parlor.

Help! Do you hear me, Jaffrey?

At this instant, Clifford himself came to the parlor.

Clifford! What is it?

Look! We can dance now, Hepzibah! We can sing, laugh, play!

She pushed past Clifford and rushed into the room. Then she returned at once, with a cry.

My God! What is to become of us?

Come! Let us leave the old house to Cousin Jaffrey!

The House of the Seven Gables

Put on your cloak and hood. Take your purse and money, and come along!

Yes . . .

In a daze, Hepzibah found herself on the stormy street, obeying Clifford's orders.

I am dreaming. It must be a dream!

At the station, they boarded a train about to leave.

R.R.

161

Clifford, this is a dream!

I have never felt so awake before!

How far, sir?

As far as that will carry us. We ride for the fun of it!

The miles flew by. Clifford looked out the windows. He talked with other people. Then his mood changed.

Come, Hepzibah! We have come far enough. Let us get off.

They left the train at a lonely station.

I'm sorry Hepzibah. You must take charge now.

O God, have mercy on us!

That night the storm ended. Uncle Venner was out by sunrise.

I never knew Miss Hepzibah so forgetful! Where is the garbage for my pig?

Good morning! Is nobody awake down there?

Not a soul. There's a strange look about the house.

Customers came to the shop and were angry to find it closed. In the town, people looked for Judge Pyncheon. They began to spread stories. The organ-grinder came again, and was warned away.

Go somewhere else! The people there are in great trouble. It is reported all over town that Judge Pyncheon has been murdered. So go away!

Later a cab stopped in front of the house and Phoebe got out.

The shop is closed!

The boy who bought gingerbread called to Phoebe.

No, no, Phoebe! There's something bad in there! Don't go in!

Worried, she ran to the back door. It opened at her knock, and a strong hand drew her inside.

Holgrave! Where are my cousins?

I should not be so glad that you have come! We met at a bad moment.

Hepzibah and Clifford are gone . . . I don't know where.

Gone! What has happened? Tell me.

Something has happened, but not to them.

Judge Pyncheon is dead in the parlor. He died of apoplexy, a common cause of death in his family.

But why are you here alone? Why haven't you opened the doors? Where are the police and doctors?

Thirty years ago Clifford's uncle died in the same way. But things were fixed by Judge Pyncheon to make Clifford seem guilty. Clifford was convicted. But I believe that Judge Pyncheon caused that man's death!

If, seeing that the judge was dead, your cousins had opened the doors and called people in, it would have helped prove that Clifford was not guilty in the earlier case.

But Clifford is not guilty!

We know that! But he ran away, and that makes him look guilty. If we could only bring him back before this death is found out!

We must not hide it a moment longer! Clifford is not guilty and God will prove it.

One thing I must say to you now, while we are alone. I love you, Phoebe!

We should not speak of such things at a time like this!

It will be a happy moment if we love one another. Do you love me, Phoebe?

You look into my heart. You know I love you!

They heard a noise . . . the front door opening . . . and footsteps. Phoebe ran to see who it was.

It is they! Thank God!

It is our own little Phoebe! And Holgrave with her!

The doctors and the police soon proved that Judge Pyncheon died of natural causes. And word spread in town that Clifford had been wrongly convicted thirty years before.

A lawyer brought further news to the cousins and Phoebe.

Word has come that Judge Pyncheon's son, traveling in Europe, died before the Judge himself did. Therefore, you, as the three last Pyncheons, will receive the Pyncheon wealth!

They decided to move from the House of the Seven Gables to the country home of the late Judge Pyncheon. On the day they were to leave, they gathered in the parlor.

That picture! It brings so many thoughts to my mind!

I could swear that as a child it told me a rich secret.

Perhaps I can bring it back. You may have hit upon this spring . . .

A secret spring! I did find it one summer afternoon . . . but I don't remember anything else!

You must have given a hint about it to Cousin Jaffrey.

And forever after, he thought you had found the secret of the missing Pyncheon wealth! He died with this in his mind!

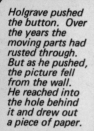

Holgrave pushed the button. Over the years the moving parts had rusted through. But as he pushed, the picture fell from the wall. He reached into the hole behind it and drew out a piece of paper.

This is the old Indian deed the Pyncheons hunted for so many years. Now that it is found, it is worth nothing.

But how did you know the secret?

How will you like to have the married name of Maule?

I have known the secret of the picture and the deed for a long time! Thomas Maule, the builder of this house, was part of my family. Each son learned the secret from his father. But now I am the only Maule left.

Then Phoebe took Uncle Venner's hand.

I insist on having you near!

There is a cottage in our new garden we are fixing up just for you, Uncle Venner!

I accept!

COMPLETE LIST OF POCKET CLASSICS AVAILABLE

CLASSICS

C 1 Black Beauty
C 2 The Call of the Wild
C 3 Dr. Jekyll and Mr. Hyde
C 4 Dracula
C 5 Frankenstein
C 6 Huckleberry Finn
C 7 Moby Dick
C 8 The Red Badge of Courage
C 9 The Time Machine
C10 Tom Sawyer
C11 Treasure Island
C12 20,000 Leagues Under the Sea
C13 The Great Adventures of Sherlock Holmes
C14 Gulliver's Travels
C15 The Hunchback of Notre Dame
C16 The Invisible Man
C17 Journey to the Center of the Earth
C18 Kidnapped
C19 The Mysterious Island
C20 The Scarlet Letter
C21 The Story of My Life
C22 A Tale of Two Cities
C23 The Three Musketeers
C24 The War of the Worlds
C25 Around the World in Eighty Days
C26 Captains Courageous
C27 A Connecticut Yankee in King Arthur's Court
C28 The Hound of the Baskervilles
C29 The House of the Seven Gables
C30 Jane Eyre
C31 The Last of the Mohicans
C32 The Best of O. Henry
C33 The Best of Poe
C34 Two Years Before the Mast
C35 White Fang
C36 Wuthering Heights
C37 Ben Hur
C38 A Christmas Carol
C39 The Food of the Gods
C40 Ivanhoe
C41 The Man in the Iron Mask
C42 The Prince and the Pauper
C43 The Prisoner of Zenda
C44 The Return of the Native
C45 Robinson Crusoe
C46 The Scarlet Pimpernel

COMPLETE LIST OF POCKET CLASSICS AVAILABLE
(cont'd)

SHAKESPEARE